POSITIVELY
izzy

TERRI LIBENSON

SCHOLASTIC INC.

ISBN 978-1-338-32597-3

12 11 10 9 8 7 6 5 4 3 2 1   18 19 20 21 22 23

Printed in the U.S.A.   40

First Scholastic printing, September 2018

Typography by Terri Libenson and Katie Fitch

To all you readers, who should never be branded
as anything except "awesome"

PROLOGUE
Brianna

I don't like labels. I just want to make that clear up front. And middle school is full of labels.

Let's be real. People aren't just one thing. Trouble is, unless you're friends with someone, you don't really know **them**, only what they're known **for**.

Take my best friend. She's known for being a great artist. And that's good. But she's so quiet, no one knows she's also sweet and funny and even kind of wacky (she has wacky parents, so that's kind of a given).

Me? Well . . .

Yeah. Ever since I moved here in kindergarten. I wouldn't even mind that label so much if . . . well, if people could look past it a little.

It's like being typecast as an actor . . . a role you're known for. That's all people expect or even want of you, 'cause it's safe.

Don't get me wrong. I like being smart. I wouldn't want to change that by flunking out or something. Then I'd be known for something **worse.**

But it'd be nice to be seen past my brains for once. 'Cause there's way more to me!

I mean, there is . . .

right?

IZZY

First of all, let's get the name thing out of the way. My older sister, Danielle, started calling me Izzy when we were little. Not because my real name is Isabelle or Isabella or anything. It's because of a knock-knock joke that I made up and repeated over and over to anyone I'd meet.

knock-knock

Who's there?

IZZY!

Izzy who?

Izzy outa the bafwoom? I hafta pee!

My mom thought the name was cute and started calling me Izzy too. Then Ashley did. Then my classmates did. So it stuck. I barely remember my real name.

The name even grew on me. Now I kinda like it. Some people are born with a name that suits them, and others—well, they have to grow into theirs or get a new one, you know? My mom always said I look more like an Izzy than my real name, so it all makes sense. It's a great stage name, too.

I'm the middle child. My older sister, Danielle, is a sophomore in high school and my younger sister, Ashley, is in sixth grade.

Dani is smart, practical, and very, very bossy. She's good at getting stuff done.

Not only is Dani bossy, but she's mega-smart too. That and being the oldest make her think **she's** our mother.

Ashley is the youngest and gets away with the most. Probably 'cause she has a way of "turning lemons into lemonade,"** as my mom says.

Yeah, it's a little irritating

*She really says "lemon shandy" . . . whatever that is.

But Ash is so sweet, even I can't resist her. Well, usually. We're only fourteen months apart ("Irish twins," although we're not Irish and not twins). We have similar minds and like to use our imaginations—mainly by making up plays and acting them out. Or, pretending we're characters from our favorite TV shows.

air kissing

My mom is an ER nurse and raises us alone. Since she works odd shifts in a hospital and is gone a lot, my sisters and I have a ton of chores we're responsible for.

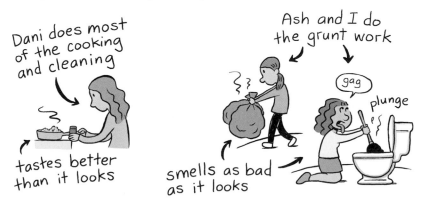

9

"Obedient Ash" doesn't mind the chores. Well, she doesn't complain, anyway. Sometimes **I** don't even mind, but mostly it's really boring or gross and I have to pretend I'm doing something more exciting to make the time go faster.

My favorite time of day is when all the chores are done and my homework (yuck) is out of the way. I have this great ritual.

① I gather all my pillows and cushions and bundle 'em on my bed

② I nestle down in my little fort

③ I write in my journal for about an hour

... or until all these pillows put me to sleep

I write about my life (so far), stories I make up, and if I'm feeling especially artsy . . . I doodle.

I'd rather do that than read like Dani or watch TV like Ashley (who doesn't study as hard as Dani but still gets decent grades!).

My grades aren't so great, which bugs my mom. She wishes I'd pay more attention in school. I wish I would, too, but there are so many more interesting things that run through my head than come out of my teachers' mouths.

Yeah, I know I could do better if I tried.

Or . . . to be totally, completely, **ginormously** honest . . .

. . . cared.

Brianna

TODAY IS SPECIAL.
IT'S A HOLIDAY.
WE HAVE A HALF DAY AT SCHOOL
(THAT'S THE HOLIDAY).

CITYWIDE TEACHERS' CONFERENCES.
MY DAD SAYS THEY'VE HELD
THESE ON THIS DAY SINCE THE
DAWN OF TIME (LIKE THE '70s).

A HALF DAY'S PRETTY MOTIVATING, SO I GET OUT OF BED AND DRESSED RIGHT AWAY. THIS SURPRISES MY DAD, WHO USUALLY HAS TO SET FOUR ALARMS AND THROW OJ IN MY FACE TO WAKE ME.

MY DAD IS THE GROGGY ONE THIS MORNING.

:snicker:

what?

pouring grapefruit juice in coffee

HE'S A HIGH SCHOOL BIOLOGY TEACHER AND COACH. THE STUDENTS LOVE HIM. WELL, THAT'S WHAT HE SAYS.

It's true. They love me.

Whatevs, Dad.

dribble

I CAN SEE IT. HE'S PATIENT AND JOKEY ... AND SLIGHTLY SARCASTIC, LIKE ME.

students out of context

Don't be jealous of my sexy gams, boys.

mix of pride and embarrassment

15

ONCE MY DAD OPENS HIS EYES,
HE STOPS POURING JUICE IN HIS
TRAVEL MUG AND SCUTTLES OVER
TO MAKE FRESH COFFEE.

SINCE HE'S A TEACHER, HE HAS
AFTERNOON CONFERENCES, SO I
PROBABLY WON'T SEE HIM UNTIL
DINNER.

MY MOM ALSO HAS A BIG EVENT LATER, SO I HAVE THE ENTIRE AFTERNOON TO MYSELF!

already plotting YouTube marathon and ice cream run with bff

chew chew

pepperoni picked off and saved for later

ON TOP OF IT, IT'S MID-MARCH AND IT'S GONNA BE IN THE 70s. SUMMER WEATHER!

Today: shorts and flip-flops

YAY

Achoo!

Tomorrow: parka and snow boots, probably

BOO

THAT MOTIVATES ME EVEN <u>MORE</u>, SO I SLURP DOWN SOME COFFEE, GRAB MORE PIZZA, AND HEAD OUT.

half cup, half filled with milk

half a slice

Happy half day!

fanks!

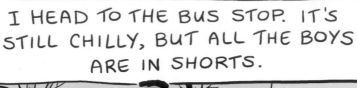

I HEAD TO THE BUS STOP. IT'S STILL CHILLY, BUT ALL THE BOYS ARE IN SHORTS.

pasty legs

goose-bumpy legs

weirdly hairy legs for a sixth grader

ONE OF THE BOYS, DEV, SEES ME AND WAVES. HE'S IN MOST OF MY CLASSES AND ALSO GETS GOOD GRADES.

Hey, Bri. Did you study for science?

Um, yeah.

distracted by Anthony Randall

ptooey

DEV ASKS ME SOMETHING ELSE (I THINK), BUT I'M MESMERIZED BY THE DRIBBLE ON ANTHONY'S CHIN.

IT'S ROUGH HAVING A CRUSH ON SUCH A POPULAR BOY. SOMETIMES EVEN I WONDER WHY I LIKE HIM.

WE GET TO SCHOOL, AND I'M RELIEVED. I NEED TO <u>FOCUS</u>!

I SEE MY BEST FRIEND, EMMIE, AT OUR LOCKERS. I'M HAPPY FOR THE DISTRACTION.

WE TALK FOR A FEW MINUTES ABOUT STUPID STUFF.

YouTube and my dad's juice mishap

half day and sister's weird new college bf

THEN IT HAPPENS.

Hi, girls.

Are you coming tonight?

Um, I dunno.

If she does, I will.

IZZY

I'm barely able to get out of bed. It's unusually warm for March, and my window is cracked open. Sooo relaxing. Well, it is until Dani shrieks from the other room.

Hurry up! You've gotta take out the trash before school.

← Dani

←delicious breeze

sigh

Looks like Ash has already gotten up. Show-off.

I have about twenty minutes before we catch the bus. First, I scribble some stuff (mostly complaints about Dani) in my journal. I'm about to put my book down when I remember the weird dream I had, and I jot that down too. I like to use my dreams for inspiration. Maybe someday they'll make great sci-fi movie plots!

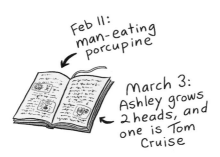

Feb 11:
man-eating
porcupine

March 3:
Ashley grows
2 heads, and
one is Tom
Cruise

Now I'm running late, so I quickly get dressed, run a comb
through my snaggy hair, and stumble into our tiny kitchen. I start
to scarf down some cereal.

Did you hear me?
I said you have to—

I heard you. Jeez!

You're procrastinating
on purpose now,
aren't you?

Why would
I do that?

slow-motion
chewing

I quickly grab all the garbage bags in the apartment and dump them into a heavier, monster-sized one. I haul it—not so gently—down the back stairs and into the alley behind the building.

I hurl the bag into the large Dumpster in the alley and then climb up the stairs. I see some neighbors in the windows. I don't mean to spy or anything, but it's hard not to notice people chewing their breakfast or watering their plants. Once I even saw a lady in the bathroom. I still can't unsee it.

Sometimes I make up stuff about the people in the building.

Yeah, that lady, Mrs. Wodaski, is a retired spy. She smiles to hide the fact that she was once a lethal gun-for-hire.

I race back upstairs to our apartment. Just in time. Ash is waiting for me at the front door. Dani must've just left. Good—I'm tired of her being on my case.

We only have half a day today. Citywide teachers' conferences or something. Ash and I are pretty pumped. We head out.

We live in a pretty big apartment complex. It's across from a cemetery. That always freaks people out when they visit for the first time, but it's actually kinda peaceful. Sometimes Ash and I go there to hang out. We like to make up stories about the people buried there. Yeah, I know that sounds creepy, but we give them **really** good stories.

My mom, the ER nurse, has this dark joke that many of her patients now live across the street from us.

My mom is a weird combination of funny and a worrywart. She worries all the time. She especially worries about me, which is kinda odd, considering I'm the middle kid and middle kids tend to go unnoticed.

Then again, I'm a bit of a "special case."

Focus is a word teachers use about me a lot.

A city bus passes, leaving a cloud of thick, smelly smog. We cough and fan it away.

Before we know it, we're lost in our heads and the school bus pulls up.

And now, back to reality.

Brianna

IN HOMEROOM, I STUDY FOR SCIENCE. EM'S "SCRITCHING" IS A DEAD GIVEAWAY SHE'S DRAWING.

click click

scritch scritch

click click clicky

RESPECT
Earn TRUST through your ACTIONS

Is that the new drama teacher?

Mrs. D? Oh yeah. I love her!

She's so much better than Mr. Randolf. I'm glad he retired.

shh!

I FEEL MY FACE FLUSH A LITTLE, BUT I SHAKE IT OFF AND GO BACK TO STUDYING.

IZZY

Ash and I get to school and separate. I head to my locker. I notice a bunch of posters for tonight's talent show hanging on the wall.

Spoiler: I made about half of them.

I'm in drama club, and we're the ones hosting the show. I'm so, so (SO) excited! Ash and I made up a three-minute skit, and I'm going to perform it. It started out as a dialogue, but Ash chickened out, so now it's a monologue. I think it's funnier as a one-woman show, anyway.

I've practiced every day for the past month, but right now I'm inwardly running through my lines. I want this down **pat**.

Standing like
a statue

Okay, got it.

I put away my backpack and take out my books. I head to homeroom, passing a group of loud girls.

One of them is Becca, my old elementary school friend. We were **really** good friends. But things kinda changed last year.

In grade school, I had three close friends: Hannah, Gabi, and Becca. We hung out all the time. At recess, we used to hide under the big slide and talk, or we'd color with chalk on the cracked sidewalk.

lopsided flower

deranged eyeball

After fifth grade, Hannah's parents moved across town and decided to send her to private school.

Then Gabi's dad lost his job, and they had to move in with her grandparents in a different state.

As for Becca . . . we hung out in the beginning of sixth grade but eventually drifted apart. Without the other two, we felt a little weird together. Plus, she joined choir and made new friends.

So that left me without a best friend this year. It's okay, I do have other friends, especially in drama club. But there's no one I'm as close to. These days I'm what my mom calls "in between friends." She says it happens to a lot of kids in middle school. Even Dani agrees.

My friend groups switched in eighth grade.

And I have totally new friends now.

Middle school sucks.

Uh... thanks.

I hope they're right.

I continue walking to homeroom. Once I get there, I take a seat and proceed to daydream the period away.

glamour bus couple

Miss Silver?

Afterward, I head to science, where I continue my daydreaming (or self-contemplating, if I want to sound more school-ish). I'm pretty bad at science.

You hit on the **BUS DRIVER?!**

She's my secret wife!

PUNCH

glamour bus couple now involved in tabloid scandal

Some kids are good at every class, like Jessica Stevens. I guess I'm pretty right-brained.

my brain

left side powered down

right side firing on all cylinders

I like creative writing, art, and drama. It shows in my grades. It's like someone drew a dividing line in the middle of my report card.

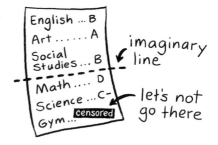

English ... B
Art ...... A
Social Studies ... B
Math .... D
Science ...C-
Gym... censored

imaginary line

let's not go there

I try to pay attention to Ms. Bloom, but her voice is so bland, I feel like I'm listening to the hum of an electric fan.

RMMMMMM

ZZZZZ

I wish I were smarter, like my sister Danielle. She gets straight As. I mean, of course she does; she's practically perfect in every way (not to quote Disney movies or anything). My mom tries hard not to compare us, but it's pretty obvious she thinks Dani has it all together.

But what's really frustrating is that Ashley gets away with murder. I guess it's third child syndrome or something. She does well in school, unlike me, but she's no Danielle.

Anyway, back to class. What was I doing again? Right! Focus!

I start thinking (sleepily) about the talent show. It starts at seven. I have to be back at school by five for rehearsal, and then Mrs. D is ordering pizza before the show.

I start to run through my lines again (partly to stay awake). The scene is really funny. And stalker-y. In it, I'm following a boy home from school without his noticing me. I'm hiding behind things, like a shed, a mailbox, and some other stuff (Ash and I spent **days** in the art room, making 'em out of foam core)... and all along I'm talking about the boy and all the ways I like him, and—

oops.

Brianna

FIRST FEW PERIODS GO BY. I'M IN SCIENCE NOW, TAKING MY TEST.

(...or trying to.)

soft humming of "Yankee Doodle"

I FINISH FIVE MINUTES EARLY. DESPITE ALL OBSTACLES, I NAILED IT.

BRNNNG

Okay, class, hand 'em in.

inward victory dance

EM AND A GIRL FROM HER ART CLASS, SARAH, ARE TALKING BY THE WATER FOUNTAIN. I GO SAY HI.

Hey, Bri.

self-squirting

NO BULLY ZONE

Hey

47

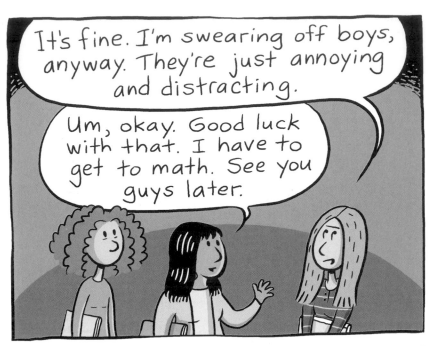

It's fine. I'm swearing off boys, anyway. They're just annoying and distracting.

Um, okay. Good luck with that. I have to get to math. See you guys later.

EM AND I WALK TO GYM TOGETHER. I'M IN HER CLASS THIS SEMESTER (I'D NEVER SEEN EM SO RELIEVED WHEN WE FOUND OUT).

Do you really believe that?

That boys are annoying? Yes.

I mean, that you can avoid them. Seems...impossible.

It's nothing. Let's just forget it.

k.

WE WALK THE REST OF THE WAY
IN SILENCE. *AWKWARD* SILENCE.

I START TO
FEEL BAD.

Em?

Yeah?

I do like Sarah.

k.

IZZY

I have two more classes to get through. English and math. I like English. Well, compared to math, anyway. The teacher, Miss Gelb, is so nice. Problem is, even though I like reading and writing, I still get average grades here. The only time I did really well was when we were asked to write our papers in the style of a play. I've been making up plays since I was six, so that kinda came naturally. I wrote a scene Ash and I made up last year about a little girl going to an amusement park with her mom for the first time. I got an A+ and a note from Miss Gelb.

"You have a knack for this!"

Today we're getting back last week's test papers on sentence structure. I have a knot in my stomach even before I see mine.

Yeah, not so surprising. There's a little note under my grade. Miss Gelb is big on notes.

"you have so much potential, Izzy. Just need more study time and focus."

There's that word again.

"focus"

Thing is, I know they're right. Half the time, I just don't care. I know I **should** care, but I'd rather be doing things I like to do. Like the talent show.

I cannot WAIT!

The bell signals it's time for math. I **really** take my time getting there. I have a test today and I didn't study. I **kind of** know the material, but . . .

I sit down. Teacher's not here yet. I hear someone whispering behind me.

uh-oh . . .

OHNONONONO!

Take-home test? I thought that was a study guide!

Huh. She doesn't think I'm serious.

Five minutes before the bell rings, Mr. Reukauf motions for me to come to his desk.

Izzy, I was checking off the papers. I didn't see yours.

Yeah... uh, I'm sorry. I kinda ... forgot it at home?

Well, I'm sorry, but I was clear about turning these in on time. Afraid I'll have to give you a zero.

Mr. Reukauf, please? I'll bring it tomorrow, I promise.

Izzy...this isn't the first time we've had this talk. You've missed numerous assignments.

I'm sorry, but a zero it is.

As he speaks, I just nod and think of every place I'd rather be than here. France. Egypt. The fiery pits of Hades.

Now I just wish I were home. Or at rehearsal (which is really where I'd like to be). I make a promise to myself that as soon as the talent show is over, I'll start focusing more on school. I will. Just need to get through today.

Luckily, the bell rings and Mr. Reukauf excuses me. My cheeks are on fire. So happy to get out of there.

After I grab my backpack from my locker, I meet up with Ashley. We walk out together. Everybody is super-excited about the half day, pushing and shoving to get as far away from school as possible.

student stampede

Ash is also excited, and she talks about going to get ice cream after our chores. My stomach both dances and lurches at the same time. I just nod dumbly and find a seat on the bus.

Stupid, smart little sister.

The bus starts to shake violently. They haven't fixed the potholes yet. For once, I don't notice. I don't even feel like distracting myself with made-up games.

I just want to be someone else.

EM AND I GO IN THE BACK ROW. WE TALK WHILE DANCING. GOOD THING WE'RE NOT GETTING GRADED.

So, are you going or not?

My mom wants me to. But I have an English paper.

Nice moves, people!

You should... just to see _them_. They're doing "Defying Gravity."

I think they're already at it.

OKAY, HERE IT IS. THE DRAMA TEACHER... MRS. D... <u>IS</u> MY MOM.

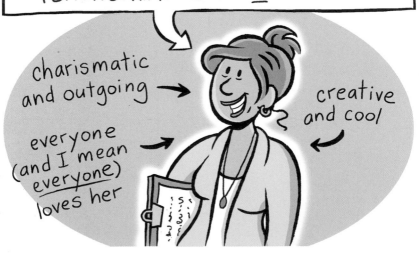

SHE TRANSFERRED HERE WHEN MR. RANDOLF "RETIRED." *

pretended to care but didn't

ear hair (yechhh)

3-week-old scruff

who the heck smokes anymore??

*[CODE FOR "SETTING THE STAGE CURTAINS ON FIRE WITH A CIGARETTE, THEN GETTING FIRED."]

MY MOM DOESN'T JUST TEACH DRAMA. SHE TEACHES EIGHTH-GRADE ENGLISH.

I know— instead of reading Shakespeare, let's perform it!

Oh! Can I be Hamlet?

Hor-atio!

WHEN THE JOB OPENED UP, SHE THOUGHT IT'D BE THE "PERFECT" OPPORTUNITY.

It'll be great to see each other in the halls.

(horrified)

Maybe we can have lunch sometimes.

I GET IT. MY PARENTS ARE DIVORCED. THEY SHARE CUSTODY. MY MOM PROBABLY FEELS GUILTY AND WANTS TO "BOND" WITH ME. SHE EVEN TRIED TO GET ME TO JOIN DRAMA (BUT GAVE UP).

C'mon, hon, open your horizons!

Mom, I hate performing!

translation: don't be "you"

IT'S NOT THAT I DON'T LOVE HER. I DO. BUT WHEN YOU'RE ALREADY LABELED AS "THE BRAIN"...

blaring neon cerebrum

...BEING IN THE SAME SCHOOL AND RELATED TO SOMEONE AS DYNAMIC AS "MRS. D" KINDA MAKES IT EVEN MORE OBVIOUS.

That's your mom? You two are so different.

←translation: she is cool and fun and you are boring and serious

GYM IS OVER AND EM AND I ARE CHANGING IN THE LOCKER ROOM. WELL, <u>SHE'S</u> CHANGING IN A BATHROOM STALL SO NO ONE WILL SEE HER.

(more obvious than changing with everyone else)

C'mon, Bri. Come tonight with Sarah and me.

Won't I be a third wheel?

Bri...

Sorry. Fine. Maybe I will. I hear Anthony is going. Oh, which means Tyler is too!

Shhhh!

Please. No one else is here. The bell's about to ring.

WE WALK TO THE STAIRWELL AND SEPARATE. EM HEADS TO THE ART ROOM TO FINISH A PROJECT.

Text me later.

Okay. Say ♫ hi to Tyyyler.

Geeeez, shhh!

rare ↑ immature moment

I'M ABOUT TO OPEN MY LOCKER WHEN I CATCH SIGHT OF MY MOM.

Bri! Hi! Am I glad to see you.

Listen, hon. I need to ask you a favor.

A <u>big</u> one.

IZZY

Ash and I arrive home. The apartment feels like a sauna. I can't believe it's March. I assume my mom is still at work since she's not around. Dani, who came home at the same time we did, cranks up the window unit and we huddle around it like a campfire.

wrrrnnnnn

↳ unearthly hum we're all used to

Ahhhhhh

↑ craving s'mores

The front door opens. Mom.

She throws me a look. Uh-oh.

Izzy, could you come in the kitchen, please?

gulp

Not sure what's going on, but I don't like it. My mom, who's normally pretty chill, looks like she's trying to keep from wringing my neck.

So...I discovered this when I was cleaning up the kitchen earlier.

blank

I say nothing.
Survival technique.

Nope.

I'm so sorry, but I totally didn't realize that it was a take-home test, I thought it was a study guide, and yeah, I shoulda studied, but I swear I won't do it again, and I'm gonna try harder, and I promise—

Stop.

I've heard all this before, Izzy. This is the final straw.

You're grounded. Three days. And I expect you to get your math grade up.

Okay...

Wait.

And yes. No talent show.

NOOOOOOOOOOOOOOOOOOOOOOOOOOOOOOOOO
OOOOOOOOOOOOOOOOO!

But...

No negotiating. I had a long shift last night and I need rest. I'm going back to bed.

M-o-o-o-m, I'm s-sorry. But it's not fair. I worked so h-hard...

I'm sorry, too, Izzy. But I'm not budging.

teardrop tidal wave

Even through my tears, I can see she means business. This is so unfair!!

I feel like I can't breathe. The **one** thing that makes me happy and I'm good at, and she took it away.

I run past her and my sisters, into my room. I slam the door. HARD.

I hear Dani through the thin walls.

Oh, you can say **that** again.

Brianna

One of the talent show entries is a group of 7th graders doing short, interrelated scenes from a play.

There's a two-person scene that's integral to it, and an actor got sick. They need a last-minute replacement.

Anyway...

What? NO!

SCRIPT

You're going to have so much fun, I promise. It's such a nice group of kids, and we're going to have pizza, and soda, and—

Okay, Mom. Let go.

Sure, okay. Here's the script. Easy-peasy. Go home and memorize. It'll be no problem with that sponge of a mind.

IZZY

I sit on my bed and stare at the wall numbly. I mean, why not? There's nothing better to do. I don't need to rehearse. I don't need to pick out performance clothes (okay, I had 'em picked out a month ago).

So I stare.

I hear my sisters whispering. You'd think by now they would know you can hear everything through these walls. It's no accident that my mom's room is on the other side of the apartment, away from ours.

She brought it on herself.

But it's not fair, Dani. Izzy's really, really good. And she practiced so much.

Maybe she should've paid as much attention in class.

Well, I'm gonna try to cheer her up.

KNOCK KNOCK

Go away, Ashley.

It's my room, too. Let me in.

Rats. She has a point. I lift myself off the bed like an old lady with rattly bones, and I open the door.

I know what you're trying to do, but it won't work. When Mom makes up her mind, that's it. So I'm just gonna be grumpy for the rest of my life.

It's not the rest of your life. It's a one-time thing.

Yeah, but it's a whole 'nother year. If they even do another show. So forget it, Ash. You can't cheer me up.

Okay, fine.

We sit in silence for a minute. Suddenly Ashley brightens and grabs my arm.

Brianna

O...M...G. THIS THING ISN'T EASY-PEASY. IT'S FIVE PAGES LONG!

And it's no lightweight piece. It's _dramatic._

doomed →

I THOUGHT THE LAST THING I'D WANNA DO IS GET UP ONSTAGE.

Nope. Last thing I wanna do is get up onstage and perform a dramatic **five-page scene!!**

OH YEAH. AND WITH ONLY A COUPLE HOURS TO MEMORIZE IT.

OH YEAH AGAIN. AND PERFORM IN FRONT OF PRACTICALLY THE WHOLE SCHOOL. _AND ANTHONY RANDALL._

crazy eyes ←

I STAND THERE FOR AN ETERNITY. THEN I COME TO MY SENSES. I NEED HELP. **NOW.**

Emmie!

I RACE TO THE BASEMENT. I CAN SMELL THE FUMES BEFORE I GET THERE.

mix of turpentine, Sharpies, and... peanut butter?

EMMIE IS PAINTING AWAY. I ALSO RECOGNIZE SARAH AND TYLER.

Bri?

Can you come into the hall?

pb&j sandwich

EMMIE STARTS CLEANING UP. I WANT TO SHAKE HER TO MAKE HER MOVE FASTER, BUT THAT'S EM. ALWAYS DELIBERATE.

(convinced it's also her hidden way to stick it to me)

turpentine

ACTUALLY, HER CALM IS STARTING TO CALM ME DOWN.

only slightly panicked

Bye, guys!

Later!

Okay, what do you need?

Come to my house. Help me practice.

You're doing it again.

Sorry. Would you *please* help me practice?

Sure. I'll text my mom.

Okay. We can still make the bus. Let's go. I mean, *please?*

ancient cell phone

Uh-oh. Bad news.

What?

My mom says I have an orthodontist appointment at two. I forgot.

ARGHH!

Maybe you can rehearse with someone else. Are you doing the scene with anyone?

Yeah, but I don't know who.

Well, sorry. I'm gonna go finish my project before my mom comes. Text you later?

uh-huh...

I MAKE IT JUST IN TIME TO CATCH THE BUS. THERE ARE STILL SOME SEATS LEFT. IT'S SO WARM, A LOT OF KIDS MUST BE WALKING.

back to full-fledged panic!

IZZY

I look at Ashley like she's grown three heads.

Are you crazy?

I'm serious. You can do it.

Rehearsal's at five. Dani will be at the library all afternoon.

And Mom sleeps like a rock.

It's true. Our mom could sleep through an earthquake—especially after a long shift. My heart starts pounding. Oh man, I want to do it. Still . . . I may not be the best kid at school, but I've never done anything . . . well, like **this**.

I can't. It's too risky.

I'll tell Mom and Dani that you're mad and to leave you alone. If they come an' check, I'll tell 'em you're asleep.

Oh wow. This could work. Then again, what if someone at the show sees me perform and tells my mom? Doubtful. Mom barely knows any of the parents, she works so much.

And what if Dani finds out? Would she snitch? If I get caught . . .

I laugh. I can't help it. I know Ash sneaks out. She leaves when Mom's asleep or at work and Dani is doing homework. She goes to her friend Meghan's house (who Mom thinks is a "bad influence") and they sneak-read her dad's dirty magazines in the bathroom. I know this 'cause Dani found out from Meghan's older sister and told me. In weird, un-Dani-like fashion, she swore me to secrecy.

I think it's partly 'cause Meghan's sister didn't want her to snitch (and take away **her** reading fun) and because . . . well, no one wants to take Ashley down. Not even Dani.

Ash is looking at me funny.

I think about it for a minute.

Actually, I've already made up my mind.

Brianna

I GET HOME AND HEAT UP SOME HAWAIIAN PIZZA FROM THE FREEZER.

WEIRDLY, GOING OVER LINES CALMS ME DOWN. PROBABLY 'CAUSE I'M USED TO MEMORIZING STUFF FOR SCHOOL.

MY DAD GETS HOME.

yes. practicing now.

ok. see u at 4:30!

FOR SOME REASON, HER ENTHUSIASM IS MAKING ME NERVOUS AGAIN.

sigh

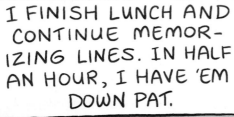

I FINISH LUNCH AND CONTINUE MEMOR-IZING LINES. IN HALF AN HOUR, I HAVE 'EM DOWN PAT.

Surprised even myself

sponge-brain to the rescue!

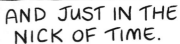

AND JUST IN THE NICK OF TIME.

♫ DING DONG

flop

IZZY

It's late afternoon when I ~~tiptoe in terror from~~ leave the apartment.

I quickly and quietly head down the empty back stairwell, through a side door into the courtyard, and down the narrow path that runs along the side of the building. My heart is pounding so hard, I'm afraid it'll burst out of my chest. I'm convinced if that happens, Mom will somehow find my ghost and ground her.

I made Ashley promise—no, **swear** up and down—that she would keep Mom and Dani away from our room. She even thought of little details, like turning on some music really low so it would seem like I was holed up, listening. Or maybe later taking a snack to me because "I refuse to come out."

Not only is my heart pounding, but my stomach is churning. I hate going behind my mom's back.

But then I think: she didn't have to ground me tonight. She **knows** how much I've been wanting this.

I pick up my pace and cut through the cemetery to save time. It's like my old friends are rooting for me.

Once I'm out of there and round the corner, I breathe a little. Thankfully, Dani and the library are in the opposite direction.

It's not just warm out. It's **hot**. I pass my favorite ice cream place, Taystee's, and suddenly I'm craving a chocolate chip cone. I'm lactose intolerant, but that stuff's worth the gas.

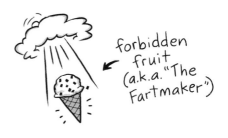

forbidden fruit (a.k.a. "The Fartmaker")

My grade school friends and I used to save our allowance and go to Taystee's every Friday after school. Even on cold days. I'd always get chocolate chip on a sugar cone. I miss that.

I realize I'm slowing down thinking about ice cream, so I pick up the pace again.

Lakefront Middle School

LAKEFRONT

(no lake)

Speaking of old times, I see Becca walking into the school with some other girls. At first, I'm surprised to see her, and then I realize she takes choir, so she's probably singing with some friends in the show.

There's a whole bunch of other kids trickling in. Some are from drama club, like me. As well as a bunch of popular kids who think they can sing. A few from band. And some I barely recognize (Lakefront is pretty big).

I walk in alone. At first, it's pretty quiet. I head toward the auditorium and hear some sounds, like furniture being moved. Mrs. D is already there, directing two eighth-grade boys to carry a dilapidated couch to the side of the stage. It drops on one side and the noise echoes all over. Not good for my pounding heart.

I join a few drama club kids up front. Becca waves hello from across the aisle. We may not be best friends anymore, but at least she's still friendly.

I wait quietly and try not to think about how I just snuck out. Funny—I'm not that nervous about getting onstage . . .

. . . but I'm **freaked out** about that!

Brianna

Just read our lines from the script.

I already memorized 'em.

Okay, then I guess we can start. You ready?

(sigh) As I'll ever be.

I WAIT FOR HIM TO START. DEV LOOKS DOWN AT HIS SHOES FOR A FEW SECONDS, THEN LOOKS UP AT ME, ALL SERIOUS.

You can't stay here, Rachel.

Why—

FIVE MINUTES LATER...

(sniff) okay... I think I'm done.

stomachache

WE TRY AGAIN.

You can't stay here, Rachel.

Why not, Sean? (um) This is my space, too. We used to (um) hang out here all the time, remember?

tired from laughter

WE DO THE WHOLE THING AND I ONLY MESS UP ONCE. I'M PRETTY PROUD OF MYSELF.

Hey, not bad. And wow, you're pretty good!

Yeah, um...

What?

Well, it's just, you're a little...

What?

Stiff?

Excuse _me_. I'm new at this.

Okay...try looking at me and not at that...really old lemonade can?

been there since summer ↳

Fine.

And maybe try to show _emotion_.

WE DO IT AGAIN.

You can't stay here, Rachel.

Why _not_, SEAN? This is MY space, too. We USED to hang out here _all_ the time...

REMEMBER??

I WISH I WASN'T DOING THIS! I WISH I WAS WRITING MY PAPER. OR THAT EM AND I WERE HANGING OUT.

Watching YouTube videos

...or playing the fridge game, "What's That Smell?"

Fine. Let's take a break. What do you want to do?

HE THINKS FOR A MOMENT.

Wanna go get some ice cream?

IZZY

Mrs. D gives us a quick welcome and passes out some photocopied programs so we can see the order. There are twenty-two performances, and I'm number five. I already knew this. I can sneak back home by eight. Ash and I made a plan. Two, in fact, in case plan A fails.

Ash will beg our mom to go out and get ice cream while Ash stays home to keep "me" company. Taystee's is in walking distance, and Mom never likes to walk outside alone in the evenings. So she'd take Dani. They do this a lot in the summer, and today **feels** like summer. While they're gone, I'd sneak back in.

If they don't go for it, I'll hide in the courtyard toolshed until they're asleep. The shed's always open, even though the custodian is supposed to keep it locked. We used to play hide-and-seek in there or spy on the neighbors.

'Course, I could be in there for a while. . . .

me

after 5-hour nap, Mom still up at midnight

Mrs. D's amplified voice startles me out of my thoughts.

Okay, people, we only have a few hours. Pizza's coming at six, so let's get started.

My heart starts pounding again.

This time, it's from excitement.

Brianna

WE HEAD TO TAYSTEE'S.
IT'S NOT FAR.

So you must <u>really</u> love your mom.

Huh?

It's kinda obvious you don't wanna be in the show. So you must really love her to do this.

right.

Truth is, I think she wants me to do this 'cause she wants me to be more like her.

More like her? Why? You're good at so many things.

(snort) Doesn't matter. She thinks I need to loosen up. She's always trying to get me into drama and stuff.

But I'm more like my dad. We both like science and math. We watch the same science documentaries on TV.

100 flavors!

Ha, this reminds me. My parents met here. Eating ice cream. Or right before or something.

They're divorced now. But they get along okay.

WAIT. WHY AM I TELLING HIM ALL THIS?

Anyway, my mom and I are cool. It's okay, I don't mind helping her out.

It's too bad you and your mom don't hang out like you and your dad do.

Yeah, I guess.

Sometimes I think she's a little jealous. But she's cool and outgoing and everyone loves her... so that can't be.

IZZY

Rehearsal. Mine goes pretty well. Gotta admit, I had a little stage fright at first—or **getting-caught** fright—but once I started the monologue, all my butterflies went away.

The only thing that went wrong was when I knocked over one of my props. But I caught it in time and didn't flub my lines.

I decide to take the prop to the art room while everyone else is rehearsing. I want to add an extra support on the bottom. There are usually some leftover wood blocks or foam core lying around.

One my way out, I hear a trumpet blast a way-out-of-tune note. They should really make a rule about not letting sixth graders do solos.

I was a little worried everyone would think my skit was dumb, but I got a lot of laughs. Maybe Miss Gelb was right. . . . Maybe I do have a knack for this.

As I round the corner, I accidentally knock into someone getting a drink at the fountain.

I make my way down the hall and down the stairs to the art room (which I smell long before I get there). I'm kinda shocked. I mean, I've missed Becca, like, a lot. I miss our friendship, our stupid pranks, our trips to the mall, and Taystee's. . . .

But I never thought she missed that stuff, too.

Brianna

I know what you mean about your mom. My parents want me to be more like them, too.

They do?

crunch

Yeah. Same for my sister. They're always on us about grades. They don't even like A minuses.

Ha! Neither do I.

Guess that's why I like drama club. Gives me a break from all that.

Oh yeah. That's how my best friend is with art.

You're like her— you're really good. At drama, I mean. I never knew that.

It's not like I go around announcing it.

Well, maybe you should.

Well, maybe you should come see our spring show.

I mean... only if you want to.

Those mnemonic devices you make up...

Yeah?

...which, by the way, are totally annoying and get stuck in my head....

That's the point!

Now I know why you do 'em. They're creative, like a song or skit.

Yeah. Makes studying a lot less boring.

Ugh. I'd rather study than get up onstage.

Hey... about that. I have an idea.

BACK ON THE DECK. WE HAVE AN HOUR UNTIL REHEARSAL. MY MOM WILL BE COMING SOON.

So have you heard of the Meisner technique?

I think my mom's mentioned it. Is that where actors play off each other's faces or something?

Sort of. Mr. Randolf taught it to us before... you know. It was the only good thing he did.

I'll say my line. Just watch my face and listen to my words. Then take your turn. *An' don't think.*

(sigh) Fine.

DEV PAUSES TO PREPARE. HE LOOKS AT HIS SHOES. I TRY TO EMPTY MY MIND. I LOOK AT HIS SHOES, TOO. THEY LOOK NEW.

Nikes?

You can't stay here, Rachel.

Why not? This is my space, too, Sean. We used to hang out here all the time, remember?

snap

OMG. I DID IT!

See? Better!

It was! It was so much better.

WE KEEP GOING UNTIL THE SCENE IS OVER. WHEN WE FINISH, I'M EXHAUSTED. BUT IN A GOOD WAY.

That was good. You did it.

I did. We did. Wow, I didn't know I had that in me.

Wanna hear something funny? I didn't either.

IZZY

I get to the art room. I'm not alone. There's a boy gluing together a couple pieces of wood. He looks familiar. I think he's in eighth grade. Kinda cute.

I giggle. I can't help it. I sound like a chipmunk, so I shut my mouth.

You're gonna watch the show?

Yeah. I have some friends in it. I mean, they can't glue two pieces of wood together like I can, but they're pretty talented.

I laugh. I like this guy.

Okay, I'd better get back. Bye...

Ben.

See you later, Ben.

Break a leg, Izzy.

Brianna

AFTER WE REHEARSE A FEW MORE TIMES, DEV HEADS HOME AND I GO TO CHANGE.

from one set of T-shirt and leggings to another

MY MIND KEEPS SWINGING BACK AND FORTH BETWEEN MY LINES AND "YANKEE DOODLE."

Argh!

HONK

snack of yogurt-covered peanuts

Hi, hon. So, you ready?

I guess.

I really appreciate this. And you're going to have fun! Once you're up there, it's such a rush, you'll forget to be nervous.

I hope you're right.

But—

Also...

Well... admittedly, I thought if you enjoyed this, maybe it would spark an interest... which would mean we'd spend more time together.

GUESS IT'S TRUE. SHE WANTS WHAT DAD AND I HAVE.

Oh.

tucking in tag

SO WHY DON'T I FEEL BETTER?

guilt

IZZY

It's almost six thirty (thirty minutes until showtime) and everyone's crowded around the big folding table in back, grabbing pizza slices like vultures. I almost get knocked down by some band kid's tuba, which I'm sure he toted over just to snag extra room.

size of a
7th grader

I manage to grab a corner slice before I'm tuba-smacked again. I walk over to my drama friends. But then I see Becca heading to the auditorium seats, and I catch up with her instead.

Why not? It's a day of taking chances. Might as well see if she's interested in hanging out again.

Hey, Izzy.

Hey. Listen, you wanna—

Her eyes suddenly glance at something behind me.

Look, your family's here.

Nah, that's impossible. They can't...

I glance back at the exit doors, and my stomach hits the floor.

She's right.
(gulp)
It's my family!

Brianna

WHEN WE ARRIVE, IT'S STILL PRETTY QUIET, EXCEPT FOR THE CREW. NOT QUITE REHEARSAL TIME.

I've gotta get everything organized. Can you help the stagehands?

Sure.

I'VE DONE STUFF LIKE THIS BEFORE. MY MOM USED TO DIRECT LOCAL THEATER.

Do you guys need anything?

Sure. Can you help carry this backdrop? It's not heavy.

THIS STUFF I DON'T MIND, UNLIKE BEING ONSTAGE.

Best backdrop we've ever made. Your mom knows her stuff.

Maybe these string lights will distract everyone from my acting.

WE FINISH SETTING UP, AND THE TALENT SHOW KIDS START TO ARRIVE. SOON, THE ROOM IS FILLED WITH ABOUT FIFTY OF 'EM.

nerves hitting me again

Hey, Bri.

Hey, Dev.

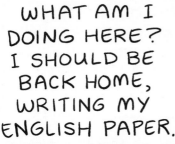

WHAT AM I DOING HERE? I SHOULD BE BACK HOME, WRITING MY ENGLISH PAPER.

YOU KNOW, SOMETHING *FUN*.

MY MOM WELCOMES US AND PASSES OUT THE PROGRAMS. DEV AND I ARE NUMBER SIX.

gossip girls (should be interesting)

uh-oh, she's good!

WE'RE CALLED UP TO REHEARSE, IN ORDER. FIRST KID IS A FLUTE SOLO.

threeeep!

Maybe sixth graders shouldn't have solos.

#5: O.M.G.

← funny

← And g<u>oo</u>d

← And has <u>props</u>

I have to follow **that**?

clap clap

clap WOO!

Okay. Dev and Brianna, you're up.

Is it too late to run away?

other kids watching and judging

WE'RE ONSTAGE. THIS IS IT. THE LIGHTS ARE DIMMED.

W-why not... um...uh...

Sean

...SEAN?

HA HA HA HA

I WISH THE GROUND WOULD OPEN UP BENEATH ME. MY FACE IS ON FIRE.

It's okay. Second time's the charm. Try again.

Look at me and listen to my words, remember?

deep breath

Okay.

WE DO IT AGAIN. THIS TIME IT WORKS. I'M A LITTLE STIFF BUT NOTHING TERRIBLE.

Good job, hon.

Not really. I wish I could drop out. It'd be easier.

Brianna Patience Davis...

really, parents?

You're not one to take the easy way. Ever. You can do this.

Fine.

Okay, #7, wipe off the Cheetos dust, you're up!

Hey, Bri, feel like practicing in one of the classrooms?

I think I'm practiced out. I just wanna do this.

Okay. No prob.

Um... You wanna walk around instead? It'll keep me from being so nervous.

Sure, yeah.

WE WALK DOWN THE HALL AND TALK ABOUT LITTLE THINGS—BOOKS, MOVIES, SNACKS...IT RELAXES ME.

easy to talk to, like Emmie

(likes Cheetos)

IZZY

I stand there with my jaw dropped to the floor. I guess it's joined my stomach.

My mom catches sight of me and glares. No, that's the wrong description. If a person could shoot flaming darts out of her eyeballs, **that's** how she looks at me.

Oh man, I'm dead.

Then Ashley sees me. Her eyes are bright red. She gives me the most apologetic look a human can give. I feel so bad for her, I'm not even mad.

eyes of
regret

Then I glance back at my mom and older sister and feel bad for me again.

erp

Before they have a chance to come over, I hurry toward them. I motion for them to follow me into an empty classroom, away from everyone else. Yeah, I'm into drama, but I really, **really** don't want this kind of scene.

Please don't kill me...

...till we get to this room.

My mom starts in.

Izzy... I'm so livid, I can barely speak. I'll give you one minute to explain yourself.

For once, the impossible happens.
I'm speechless.

Mom, I told you. It's not Izzy's fault. I'm the one who—

I want to hear it from Izzy.

I take a deep, shaky breath and let it all out.

I'm so, so sorry, I really am, but I've been practicing for this forever, and I'm really good, and you should've heard the clapping in rehearsal, and I know I was wrong, and you can punish me for a year, but just give me a chance!

No. We're going home.

Ashley starts to cry. I swear she takes on other people's feelings so much, she should have multiple personalities.

snot coming out of her nose

I glance at Dani. She's looking at Ashley. And starting to feel bad, I can tell. Dani looks back at me. That's when I lose it. Everyone's crying except my mom, who looks like she just wants to take a two-day nap.

(fed-up sigh)

You can all cry at home. Come on, let's go.

W-wait. How'd you find out?

I see Dani look away.

She whirls around, her own eyes shooting darts. Scratch that.
Bullets.

I came home
from the library
and your dishes
from lunch were
still in the sink.

I went to get you.
Well, there was Ashley.
But there <u>you</u> weren't.

Ash tried to cover
for you, but come on.
I'm not stupid.

So you
told??

Girls...

I'm dumbstruck. It's the first time Dani has ever said anything like this. Mom and Ash are shocked, too.

Dani looks down.

I'm still pretty fired up. I also feel like I got socked in the gut. Her words hit. Hard.

But a strange thing happens. My anger starts to melt. Not all at once but kinda slowly, like dripping candle wax (okay, maybe quicker than that, but you get my point).

Actors and playwrights are supposed to put themselves in other people's shoes. I always try to do that. It's usually pretty easy for me. But never with Dani.

Usually Dani's so bossy and demanding that I can't see straight. But I don't think I've ever tried to look past all that.

For once, I try putting myself in her place.

And all **I've** ever done is make it harder for both of them.
Even if I don't mean to.

Wow. What's that word that Miss Gelb had us define early in the year? **Epiphany.** I think I'm having one.

I take a deep breath and try to look my sister in the eye.

Then I say the most mature thing I've probably ever said in my life.

I'm sorry, Dani. You were right to be mad.

I think if she could faint from shock, she would. Instead, she stays quiet. But she smiles, a little.

My mom puts her arm around Dani's shoulders.

Sometimes I forget how much you all take on.

We'll work on that, okay?

I'm so disappointed, I'm unable to move. The talent show! But I'm also feeling pretty ashamed, so I force my feet toward the door.

Huh?

Brianna

SHOWTIME! IT'S SEVEN O'CLOCK AND THE PLACE IS PACKED. I SEE MY DAD CHATTING WITH SOME TEACHER FRIENDS.

I SEE EMMIE AND SARAH SEATED ON THE LEFT.

pang of jealousy

pang of guilt for the jealousy

AND ANTHONY, TYLER ROSS, JOE LUNGO, AND THE *ENTIRE BASKET-BALL TEAM* SMACK-DAB IN THE MIDDLE.

What did I get myself into?

nowhere to spit

MY MOM SAYS A FEW FUNNY WELCOMING REMARKS AND COMPLIMENTS OUR "TALENT" AND "HARD WORK." YEAH, YEAH. THEN SHE CALLS UP THE FIRST ACT.

FIRST HALF HOUR FLIES. FLUTE GIRL DOES HER THING. BETTER THIS TIME. I DON'T FEEL LIKE RIPPING OUT MY EARS.

SECOND ACT IS PRETTY GOOD. THIRD ACT: I MAY HAVE SPOKEN TOO SOON ABOUT MY EARS.

But ever since my mom came to this school... and my bff started making new friends... and now being roped into <u>this</u>...

I feel like everything is, I dunno, out of my control.

OMG, <u>sorry</u>! I just unloaded on you.

That's okay.

I like it.

EVEN THOUGH I'M NERVOUS, I CAN'T HELP IT. I SMILE.

Thanks, Dev. You're pretty cool.

Yeah... so are you.

IZZY

But she should be in the talent show.

What?

What?

She's been practicing forever. And she's good. I hear her sometimes.

She does?

She's worked really hard.

At this. Not at her other subjects.

I know it goes against all logic, but I think it's the right thing...for Izzy. And I think she'll try harder afterward.

My jaw is on the floor again. So is Ashley's.
Mom gives me a long look.

Her face softens a little.
The fiery darts disappear.

Just. This. Once.

But as soon as we get home...

I squeal and hug my mom so hard she almost falls over. Ash laughs and Dani snorts.

I know. I'm grounded for eternity.

And then some.

Brianna

DEV AND I WAIT THROUGH THE NEXT TWO ACTS. THE FOURTH ONE GOES SMOOTHLY.

clap clap clap

I PEEK AT THE FIFTH ONE. GIRL DOES A SOLO ACT AND IT'S EVEN BETTER THAN IN REHEARSAL.

We have to follow *that?*

CLAP CLAP WOO! yeah

BEFORE HE CAN RESPOND, WE'RE CALLED UP.

WE HEAD DOWNSTAGE AS MY MOM INTRODUCES US.

...Dev Devar and Brianna Davis performing another scene from "The Lucky Ones."

POLITE CLAPPING. ALSO HOOTS FOR DEV. MY MOM PASSES US WITH A WINK, AND SUDDENLY WE'RE ALONE IN THE SPOTLIGHT.

I'M GLAD IT'S SO DARK IN THE AUDIENCE THAT I CAN'T SEE ANYONE.

You can't stay here, Rachel.

frozen

AN AWKWARD MOMENT PASSES. DEV TRIES AGAIN.

You can't stay here, Rachel.

I'M HORRIFIED. OH SURE, *THAT'S* THE MOMENT THE MIKE GOES CRAZY AND EMITS DEAFENING FEEDBACK.

ONCE THE MIKE IS FIXED, WE START OVER. BUT NOT UNTIL DEV MOTIONS TO ME.

APPARENTLY WE CAN READ MINDS NOW.

178

WE GO ON UNTIL THE SCENE IS OVER. WHEN IT IS, I BARELY REALIZE IT.

WE DID IT. AND IT WAS ...FUN!

IZZY

I've stopped "seeing" my family and everyone else in the audience. Partly 'cause it's so dark, but mainly because I'm focused.

Somewhere out there, people are laughing. That's good. It gets me more pumped.

When I finish the scene, I get a lot of clapping and some cheers. The cheers are from my family. I'd recognize their screeches anywhere.

I feel great, like I climbed a mountain and am floating down. I did my own thing and it made it that much sweeter.

I don't care if I **am** grounded for an eternity.

It was worth it.

Brianna

I TALK WITH SOME OF THE KIDS BACKSTAGE DURING THE REST OF THE SHOW.

I can't believe I didn't pass out.

I thought I was gonna drop my flute, my hands were so sweaty.

Everyone's okay as long as they don't do what Kyle Duncan did last year.

What'd he do?

Sneezed and farted at the same time.

Got him a standing ovation, though.

I remember when Lizzie Freed did a dance routine, and her retainer fell out and she <u>stepped</u> on it.

Why the heck was she <u>wearing</u> it?

I should've come last year. I probably would've been a lot less nervous.

giggle

AFTER THE SHOW, EVERYONE SCATTERS TO JOIN THEIR FAMILIES. I HANG BACK TO HELP CLEAN UP.

Hey, Bri, you ready? My parents can take us.

Yeah, just gimme a few minutes to tell my mom and dad.

Guys, stack the chairs in rows. Good. And— Oh, hey, hon! Great job tonight.

Thanks. Em invited me for ice cream.

Okay. I have to finish here, anyway.

Wait. Honey?

So now that you're a stage "veteran," what do you think about doing something like this again. Maybe... drama club?

Well, I did have fun tonight. And you were right—once I got up there and into it, I wasn't so nervous.

That's great!

But...

(sigh) Mom... this is <u>your</u> thing, not mine. I mean, I'm glad I did it, but I doubt I'll do it again.

I see.

Sorry you're disappointed.

! snorf

How could I ever be disappointed in you, Bri? You give <u>everything</u> your 110 percent. I'm just glad you stepped out of your comfort zone for once.

The only thing I'm disappointed about is that we won't be able to share this.

Well, maybe we can do more stuff together outside of school.

Sure. I think we can make more of an effort.

Well, you enjoy practical things... and getting things done. What if you joined stage tech?

Stage tech? Huh.

Stage tech? Funny, Sarah and I were talking about doing that next year. Like painting scenery.

Yeah, it'd be fun if you did it, too!

Well... I guess we can talk about this at Taystee's. Okay if I go with Em and Sarah?

Yep, but you know the rule.

Bring you home a pint of Rocky Road.

WE START TO LEAVE. BUT THEN I CATCH DEV WALKING OUT WITH HIS FAMILY.

EXIT

This week:

Hang on...

IZZY

Instead of hanging out with everyone backstage, I decide to join my family in the audience for the rest of the show. There are no more seats, so Ash lets me share hers.

looking like conjoined twins

Overall, it's a pretty good show. Lots of musical acts and skits. There's one weird but entertaining juggling act with tacos (which doesn't end well).

SPLORT

S'okay, I have more!

When it's over, we get up and start to head out. I want to say bye to my friends, but I'm pretty sure my mom wants me behind bars ASAP.

Hey, Izzy, wait!

A bunch of us are going to Taystee's to celebrate. Wanna come?

Oh. Uh...

Sorry, Becca. I can't.

Go ahead, Izzy.

No, it's okay.

Go ahead. It's your night. We'll start everything tomorrow.

Cool! Thanks, Mrs. Silver!

Great to see you again, Becca. It's been awhile.

Dani was right.
You were wonderful!
I never realized how
much you enjoy this.
And you really looked
like you loved it up there.

BUT...

yeah...

You CANNOT go to drama club until you get your grades up. We'll discuss in detail later.

Okay.

We'll also discuss your and Ashley's punishments.

gulp

Dani, Ash, I'll pull the car around. Izzy, be back in an hour, please.

Okay, Mom.

Well, at least we're in this together.

Sorta. I still have to get my grades up.

197

I might be able to help with that.

I'll make a deal, Iz. You make more of an effort to help with chores, and I'll tutor you.

Really?

Yeah, but just a warning... I'm tough.

No kidding.

We all head outside. Dani and Ash get in Mom's car and drive home. I walk over to Becca, who's hanging out with a group of kids.

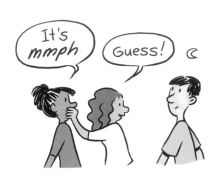

It's *mmph*

Guess!

Let's see. Izzy rhymes with fizzy. And you're pretty bubbly an' fun... like fizz. So...a float?

haha! Nope.

Anyway, Izzy isn't my real name.

What is it, Isabelle?

Nope.

Dev was really great about helping me with the scene. Mind if I invite him along?

Okay. But I thought you "swore off" boys.

yeah, yeah

He's cooler than I thought. And nice.

And cute.

What? He is. And I think he likes you, Bri.

Forget it. She only has eyes for Anthony.

I HEAD BACK TO EM AND SARAH.

Is he coming?

He can't. It's okay, let's go.

Y'know, I was just thinking. Now people are gonna see you differently.

What do you mean?

No one expected <u>you</u> to perform onstage... even with your mom in charge.
You might not be known as "The Brain" anymore.

haha! Maybe.

Epilogue: Brianna

IT'S THE LAST SUNDAY OF THE MONTH. THAT MEANS ONE THING:

Family Brunch!

MY GRANDMA, AUNTS, AND COUSINS ROTATE HOMES AND EVERYONE BRINGS SOMETHING.

our usual, "blintz soufflé"

my aunt's weird specialty, "Breakfast Beans"

bagels

BEEN DOING THIS SINCE WE MOVED BACK FROM ATLANTA.

TODAY, WE'RE HOSTING.

pouring batter on blintzes (tastes better than it looks)

cleaning frenzy

Dad's house

Taystee's (yum)

Mom's condo (3 blocks away)

IT'S A PAIN TO TREK BACK AND FORTH, BUT AT LEAST MY PARENTS LIVE CLOSE TO EACH OTHER.

I MENTIONED BEFORE, THEY STILL GET ALONG.

Is Dad coming?

Not today. He has a million papers to grade.

Oops, we'd better get that in the oven. They'll be here soon. Especially you-know-who.

snort

PROBABLY 'CAUSE THEY'VE KNOWN EACH OTHER SINCE THEY WERE KIDS.

MY ONE AUNT IS <u>ALWAYS</u> PUNCTUAL. SHE AND MY UNCLE ARE BOTH LAWYERS. THEY HAVE ONE SON.

Bradley (named after my late grandpa) →

trying to grow scruff

never smiles

THEY LIVE IN A HUGE HOUSE THAT MY MOM CALLS A "McMANSION." ALL THE HOMES ARE GINORMOUS AND LOOK ALIKE.

Same homes, different colors

McTree

MY AUNT'S WOUND UP PRETTY TIGHT, SO MY MOM LIKES TO MAKE HER LAUGH. IT'S WORTH THE EFFORT.

Remember when I told you I slipped a Xanax in Mom's oatmeal and you believed me?

BWAHAHAHA!

laughs like it's been held in for 3 years

MY OTHER AUNT IS THE OPPOSITE — LAID-BACK AND KIND OF A HIPPIE.

"Peacekeeper" of the family

Is a teacher, like my dad (at an elementary school)

wears pretty peasant blouses

SHE AND MY MOM HAVE ALWAYS BEEN CLOSE. SHE LIVES WITH HER PARTNER AND KIDS IN A SUBURB A FEW HOURS AWAY.

Tina

Molly (always looks bored)

Gabriella (always looks like she stuck her finger in a socket)

MY GRANDMA'S COMING, TOO. SHE'S REALLY SWEET. GRAM WAS SO UPSET SHE WAS WORKING AND COULDN'T SEE ME PERFORM LAST WEEK.

I'm so, so sorry, honey. Did your dad record it?

That's okay, Gram. And yeah, unfortunately he did.

TWENTY MINUTES LATER, EVERYTHING IS READY. MOM AMAZED HERSELF.

Don't remember the last time we didn't spill the oj or scorch the coffee.

"We"?

DING DONG

They're all here.

At once? A double miracle.

EVERYONE SWARMS AROUND THE TABLE. WE DON'T WASTE TIME IN THIS FAMILY.

Oh! I left dessert in the car.

Dessert? It's <u>brunch</u>, Gram.

I got it for your mom. Her birthday's in a few days and I wanted us to celebrate all together.

Oh. I can get it.

GRAM GIVES ME THE KEYS AND I GRAB THE GROCERY BAG FROM HER CAR.